Billie Holiday

Muñoz & Sampayo

with an afterword by
Stanley Crouch

FANTAGRAPHICS BOOKS

Fantagraphics Books

7563 Lake City Way NE
Seattle, WA 98115

Translated by Katy MacRae, Robert Boyd, and Kim Thompson.
Lettered by James Greer.
Designed by Mark Thompson.
Published by Kim Thompson and Gary Groth.

First Fantagraphics Books edition: March, 1993.

10 9 8 7 6 5 4 3 2 1

ISBN: 0-56097-085-5

Printed by Castle-Pierce Co. in the United States of America

NEW YORK, SATURDAY, 11:30 PM

LISA, I NEED ALL THE FACTS YOU'VE GOT ON HOLIDAY, BILLIE, JAZZ VOCALIST, FEMALE, BLACK, DEAD AT AGE 44, 30 YEARS AGO.

SEND IT OVER TO MY SCREEN. OH, I NEED SOME PHOTOS, TOO, AND -- ABOVE ALL -- MUSIC. I NEED TO HEAR THIS WOMAN'S SINGING.

BILLIE HOLIDAY... THEY MIGHT'VE SPRUNG THIS ASSIGNMENT ON ME EARLIER... AND ME HAVING NO IDEA WHO SHE IS.

I GOT YOU THE DOPE ON THIS BILLIE PERSON.

OKAY, GO AHEAD AND TAKE OFF, I'LL BE ON THIS ALL NIGHT. THEY WANT FINAL COPY BY DAWN.

SUNDAY, 12:25 AM.

...PROSTITUTE, ALCOHOLIC, DRUG ADDICT, DIED YOUNG... "THE FLOWER OF THE AGE"... WORE A FLOWER IN HER HAIR...

RRR...

HER LOVE LIFE WAS ON THE UNHAPPY SIDE.

RRRRRooo

MAKE THAT CHAOTIC. BETTER YET, CRIPPLED. THAT'S IT: CRIPPLED.

HEY, YOU'RE NEW HERE, RIGHT?

NO, SIR. BEEN HERE 17 YEARS.

"SHE HAD NO LUCK WITH MEN: THEY ALL PARTOOK OF THE FORTUNE SHE EVENTUALLY EARNED."

"THE TABLOIDS EMPHASIZED THOSE ASPECTS OF HER LIFE TO THE EXCLUSION OF HER MUSIC."

DON'T LEAVE ME, RUFUS!

"IT'S THE LAW OF SUPPLY AND DEMAND. THERE'S A PUBLIC THAT WANTS THAT KIND OF STUFF."

TAKE THAT, WHORE!

"THERE'S ANOTHER PUBLIC THAT PRE-TENDS IT DOESN'T, AND WON'T ACCEPT IT UNLESS IT'S DISGUISED."

CONSIDER IT A GOODBYE PRESENT,

"THIS LATTER AUDIENCE IS THE ONE THAT BUYS OUR PAPERS, THAT LETS US TURN A PROFIT."

STUPID BITCH! YOU AREN'T GON-NA KILL ANYONE ... NOT ME, NOT YOURSELF!

7

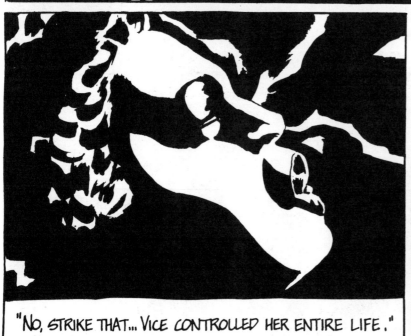

"HER INITIAL ADDICTION LED HER TO ALL HER OTHER ADDICTIONS."

"OR THIS: IN HER LATTER YEARS, ONE COULD HEAR THE (SEARING) RASP OF ALCOHOL. (OF HER ALCOHOLISM?)"

"SHE DIED, VICTIM OF... VICTIM OF... WHAT THE HELL *DID* SHE DIE OF, COME TO THINK OF IT?"

WAIT UP FOR ME. HOPEFULLY I'LL WRAP IT UP EARLY. OK, SURE.

SUNDAY, 3:08 AM, AT THE OTHER END OF THE ISLAND.

...PERHAPS THEY DON'T REMEMBER HER BECAUSE SHE DIED SO LONG AGO.

Click

ON A DAY LIKE TODAY, 30 YEARS AGO, BILLIE HOLIDAY.

SHE WAS AN IDOL FOR BLACK AMERICANS AND A HEROINE OF THE LOVE SONG: BILLIE HOLIDAY.

You might find th' right time th' right time for kissin'

THIS MAN IS WELL ACQUAINTED WITH BILLIE HOLIDAY, DESPITE HIS IGNORANCE OF A CERTAIN EPISODE FIFTY-ODD YEARS AGO...

...ANYWAY, YOU KNOW I NEED INSTANT GRATIFICATION ... I'M GOING TO FIND ME ANOTHER MAN.

WAIT, WAIT! AND ABOVE ALL DON'T DRINK THAT BOTTLE OF POMERY.

Fake Books.

Fake Graphic Novels

She has fake tits, too.

"ON ONE OCCASION SHE WAS ARRESTED WITH LESTER YOUNG FOR..."

ALL RIGHT, WHAT'S GOING ON HERE?

THESE NIGGERS WERE THROWING DIRT ON THE HOOD OF MY CAB.

WHO'S GONNA CLEAN UP THIS MESS? TWO STAINS ... NOT ONE, TWO, AND ON MY NEW FINISH.

THAT'S NOT TRUE. HE'S LYING.

I KNOW YOU PEOPLE—YOU'RE ANIMALS. NOW STAY WHERE I CAN SEE YOU.

"AND OCCASIONALLY SET FREE NO QUESTIONS ASKED..."

17

THE MAN EVEN REMEMBERED HER SMILE, THE WAY SHE LOOKED.

BUT HE DOESN'T KNOW WHAT HAPPENS AFTER HIS MEMORY ENDS.

I DON'T UNDERSTAND, BUT ... OKAY.

"... THE TROOPS OF GENERAL BER- GONZZONI HAVE BEEN CRUSHED IN GUADALA- JARA, "

NOW THAT'S WHAT I LIKE: A GOOD LITTLE GIRL.

VERY GOOD. NOW LET'S FOLD THE CLOTHES CARE- FULLY.

"SHE HERSELF COULD NOT EX- PLAIN HOW SHE'D ENDED UP IN THIS SITUATION."

WAS THAT ALL YOU WANTED?

SO WHAT DO WE DO NEXT?

WE DO THIS:

IF YOU'RE SO FOND OF FAGGOTS ...

"... IT'S TIME SOME- ONE REMINDED YOU WHAT A REAL MAN IS LIKE.

NOR DOES THE JOURNALIST KNOW WHAT HAPPENED. ONLY BILLIE DOES.

YOU'LL HAVE TO GET OUT OF THIS YOURSELF, OR WITH YOUR PANSY SAX PLAYER.

GOOD-BYE, ELEANOR. WITH YOUR JEWELRY AND CAR, I FIGURE I'M PAID IN FULL.

WHY, RUFUS... WHY?

HEY, GET A LOAD OF THIS!

...NEGRO, SAYS SHE WAS ATTACKED, THAT SHE'S A FAMOUS SINGER, A WOMAN WITH MONEY.

BEING RICH DOESN'T MATTER WHEN YOU'RE NAKED, NIGGER ...ESPECIALLY A HOT NUMBER LIKE YOU.

SO YOU'RE A FAMOUS SINGER, HUH? GREAT ... WE'LL GET OUR NAMES IN THE PAPERS.

I ALWAYS ENJOYED THE HIGH-SPIRITED PLAYFULNESS OF FAMOUS SINGERS.

FRESH MEAT!

LOOK, HERE'S SOME MORE FAMOUS SINGERS.

WOULD YOU GIVE ME SOMETHING TO COVER MYSELF WITH?

REGRETTABLY, I AM OBLIGED TO DO SO.

IT'S BILLIE HOLIDAY, A FAMOUS SINGER.

LET'S SEE IF YOU CAN EXPLAIN YOUR SCANTY ATTIRE NOW.

AND I'M ELEANOR ROOSEVELT.

... I WAS NAKED 'CAUSE I FELT LIKE IT, OKAY?

NEW YORK, 5:00 AM.

YEARS LATER, SHE MADE HER FILM DEBUT IN AN ENORMOUS HOLLYWOOD PRODUCTION.

ON THE OTHER END OF THE ISLAND. 5:00 AM.

I SAW THAT MOVIE. SHE PLAYED A MAID IN IT.

"...AND I RECOGNIZED HER ON THE SCREEN."

DADDY...

WHADDYA WANT?

NEW ORLEANS
CORDOVA
BILLIE HOL
LOUIS ARMSTR
NEXT WEEK: T ORCHE

THIS BABY IS A DEAD WEIGHT, DRAGGIN' ME DOWN...

I KNOW THAT LADY WHO SINGS--I CHANGED THE WHEEL ON HER CAR AND SHE GAVE A DOLLAR TO ME AND MY FRIEND...

FIRST: SHE AIN'T NO LADY, SHE'S A NIGGER. YOU REMEMBER THAT, SON. AND SECOND...

27

WHAT'S GOING ON WITH BILLIE?

THEY'RE NARCOTICS AGENTS. IF YOU INTERFERE, YOU'LL GET BURNED. DON'T FORGET YOU'RE BLACK.

I WON'T FORGET, NO SIR. HOW COULD I?

IN THE INSPECTOR'S OFFICE, SHE APPEARED ARROGANT.

WITH YOUR PAST, YOU'RE THE ONE WHO HAS NO RIGHTS.

YOU'VE GOT NO RIGHT! NONE!

I'M AN ARTIST. I WORK. THAT'S MY PAST. AND THE FACT IS, I DON'T HAVE ANY DOPE ON ME.

ON YOU, NO. INSIDE, YES. WE'VE GOT YOUR DEALER. "ARTIST" -- GIVE ME A FUCKIN' BREAK ALREADY.

YOU SON OF A BITCH!

LOCK HER UP FOR ASSAULTING AN OFFICER.

AFTER YOU, WHORE!

SEVEN, SIX ....

ALMOST DAYBREAK: 5:45 AM.

... FOUR, ZERO.

JOHH, YOU GOT A CALL.

JOHH, IT'S ALACK ... DO ME A FAVOR AND RE-FRESH MY MEMORY. WHO WAS PRES?

GOOD QUESTION ... LESTER YOUNG. ONE OF US, THE BEST IN HIS DAY. BIG, VERY BIG.

A FRIEND JUST ASKED ME WHO PRES WAS.

I DIDN'T KNOW THAT.

TODAY IS THE 30th ANNIVERSARY OF BILLIE HOLIDAY'S DEATH.

OF COURSE YOU DIDN'T.

"HE WAS WASHED UP AND SHOWED UP ON THE SET WEARING HIS SLIPPERS."

"PRES WAS FINISHED, NOTHING BUT A SHELL, BUT THE MOMENT OF THE MUSICAL ENCOUNTER WAS EXTRAORDINARY."

WE'VE LOST IT, SISTER. THIS IS THE END.

I'M IN A BAR... I'M... I'M NOT GONNA WAIT FOR YOU ANY LONGER.

SHE'S -- I MEAN SHE WAS A REMARKABLE WOMAN. YOU HAVE NO IDEA.

I'M GONNA FUCK SOMEONE RIGHT HERE IN THE BAR.

WE CAN DO IT HERE IF YOU WANT TO.

GOOD. I'LL CALL YOU AS SOON AS YOU'RE DONE.

LISTEN, THIS IS A RESPECTABLE PLACE. WE'VE GOT ROOMS IN BACK FOR *THAT*.

AND THEN LESTER YOUNG DIED, BLAH, BLAH, BLAH ... NOTHING HERE OF ANY INTEREST.

"HE SPENT THE LAST FEW MONTHS OF HIS LIFE DRINKING AND LISTENING TO SINATRA RECORDS."

"BILLIE TOOK THE BLOW VERY BADLY."

LADY ... LESTER DIED TONIGHT.

LESTER ...

GOOD EVE-NING, MISS HOLIDAY.

GOOD EVENING, CELIA.

FUCK ALL
OF YOU!

THAT'S IT,
ASSHOLE,
YOU'RE FIRED.

I'VE ALREADY
CALLED THE
POLICE.

THIS ...
IS ...
SONG ...

ASLEEP, SHE
WOULD DREAM OF
A GLORIOUS,
UNTOUCHABLE
PAST...

NEW YORK, 6:15 AM

"... IN THE DAYS WHEN SHE WAS THE QUEEN. BUT A QUEEN WHO NEVER FORGOT HER ROOTS, A QUEEN WITH A GOOD DEAL OF RESENTMENT... "

I'M GOING TO SING A SONG ABOUT A FRUIT ...

... A STRANGE FRUIT THAT GROWS IN THE TREES DOWN SOUTH.

THE BODY OF A HANGED MAN, AN UPPITY NEGRO ... LIKE ME.

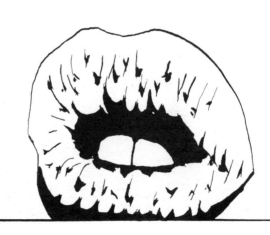

NEW YORK, SUNDAY MORNING. THE SUNDAY ARTS SECTION.

AND HERE'S THE QUESTION OF HER DEATH... YES, YES... A LEGITIMATE SUBJECT TO COVER... GOOD...

BOOKS

LADIES AND GENTLEMEN: BILLIE HOLIDAY.

I don't know why but I'm feelin' so sad...

...the night is cold, I'm so alone...

44

NEW YORK, JUNE 12.

ELEANOR HOLIDAY'S ROOM.

ELEANOR HOLIDAY YOU ARE CHARGED WITH POSSESSION OF HEROIN.

YOU HAVE THE RIGHT TO REMAIN SILENT; YOU HAVE THE RIGHT TO AN ATTORNEY...GET HER PRINTS.

YOU ARE ADVISED THAT ANYTHING YOU SAY MAY BE USED AGAINST YOU...

HOW COULD SHE HAVE ANY HEROIN? SHE'S BEEN HERE FOR THE PAST TWO WEEKS.

WE'LL POST A TWENTY-FOUR HOUR GUARD WITH FOUR SHIFTS OF SIX HOURS EACH. SHE'S FORBIDDEN TO LEAVE THIS ROOM.

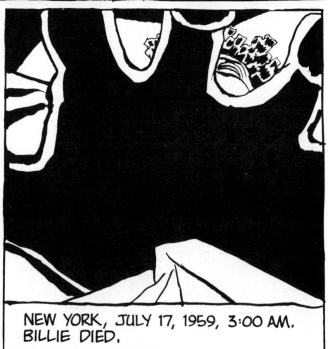

NEW YORK, JULY 17 12 HOURS EARLIER.

BILLIE HOLIDAY .... THEY JUST RELEASED A CD BOXED SET OF HERS .... HAVE TO PICK IT UP ON MONDAY.

HOW MUCH DO I HAVE ON ME? I GUESS I SHOULD GIVE HER A CALL.

YEP, I'M GONNA BUY THAT SET....

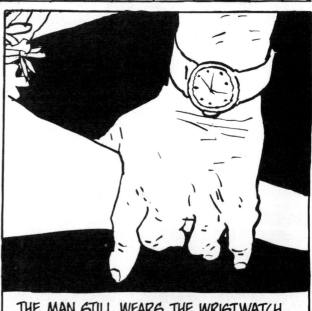

THE MAN STILL WEARS THE WRISTWATCH THAT WAS IN THE NEWSPAPER PHOTOGRAPH.

THE SAME ONE THAT TOLD HIM IT WAS THREE O'CLOCK IN THE MORNING ON JULY 17, 1959 ...

... AND WHICH CONFIRMED THAT, HIS CHARGE HAVING DIED, HE COULD RETURN HOME THREE HOURS EARLY.

BILLIE HOLIDAY
1915
1959
(ARTIST)

I KNEW HER.

SO DID I.

FIN

The Invincible

BILLIE HOLIDAY's

life and art are often victims of racial, sociological, psycho-analytic and feminist sentimentality. She is used, as are her interpretations of songs, to justify, validate, and pump up more than a few theories about the relationship of African-Americans and women to American society. One will always hear how much she was exploited, how pathetic a character she was. How she was betrayed by an endless stream of prover-bially *no good* men, how she would have been much happier and much more successful had she been white and as deeply talented. Some will say she was obviously masochistic and given to self-destruction. According to one writer, a famous impresario implied that she used all the terrible things that happened to her as an excuse for irresponsible behavior (this may be part of what one might call *hip paternalism* — the Kentucky colonel in dark glasses deriding the "nigras" in

a bastardization of their own slang, a perpetual phenomenon in the jazz world).

Others will say that a plot has always existed, the intent of which has been to break the spirits and backs of African-Americans, and that the ease with which heroin was able to get into the black community and *stay* there is a grotesque realization of said plot. Hence: that grand and tan dame of popular song elevated to high art was a victim. Still others might say she was naive and young, in the way that even tough women can be, when she first became addicted to heroin, and that the drug was an insufficient alternative to the weights of racism, poverty and disregard. Finally, the most political will put it all together as part of an ongoing indictment against capitalism and the bullfrog social eloquence of American democracy. In short: flam.

But in many ways, all of that may be too simplistic, for what made Billie Holiday important was her extraordinary musical talent combined with the fact that she arrived at a time when the gifts she had could be cultivated, documented and influential. Though she transformed Tin Pan Alley dross to art song gold, her vocal talents would probably never have amounted to much had she been born in the same circum-stances in Europe. Billie couldn't read, had a voice neither large nor strong, with a range of little more than a tenth, which receded to a little more than an octave when she made some of her finest recordings in the later years of her life (conse-quently, she was forced, like the aged Matisse, even further into herself and her talent, stripping away the excesses of lightweight tunes in favor of a spare and often lilting lyricism).

In more than a few ways, she personifies the reasons why jazz has become so significant, for it is the most democratic of Western musics; in the sense that it has been developed by every imaginable type of musician, from the most primitive to the most urbane, aesthetically paralleling, in some respects, the development of modern America itself. Jazz allows for any kind of talent that can produce coherent musical state-ments. If one can make it happen, one's music is valid. The richness of the music is often due to the fact that it has always had room for the individual, more room than had existed before in Western music.

Though Billie may not initially have reminded listeners of either of her mentors — Louis Armstrong and Bessie Smith — she was grounded in their styles and developed her own direction from the looseness of Armstrong's phrasing and Bessie's powerful, undaunted elegance. Armstrong, the seer of modern American improvisational music, is often thought of as a musician who tended to come right down on the beat, as with his characteristic popping of staccato quarter notes, but that is far from the whole story. If one hears his versions

Sound Of SWING

of "I Gotta Right To Sing The Blues," his floating, wordless vocal on "West End Blues," or the 1932 rendition of "Mahogany Hall Stomp," it is obvious that Armstrong taught Lester Young as well as Holiday how to create a swing which seemed liberated from the overt beat and tempo. Armstrong, like Bessie Smith, was a master of inflection, capable of coming down on a note in almost endless ways, to the extent that one tone could jab, bite, simmer, dissolve, swell, yelp, sizzle, or grind. But where both Armstrong and Smith were given to the grand gesture, or identified by it, Holiday seems to have been more introspective, even delicate, in pursuit of the kind of dignity the musicians of the thirties such as Ellington, Lunceford, Basie and others were striving for — a freedom from the stage conventions imposed on musicians like Armstrong. (This is not to say that the music she made was devoid of humor, joy, celebration or the bumptious optimism of swing; in the funnin' satire of "A Fine Romance," for example, she swings over the beat with a buoyancy that sparks her fellow musicians.)

Billie Holiday is, of course, an American artist and one who could only have developed in the way she did here. If she hadn't the talent to stylize experience and imagination, empathy and dread, all of the bouts with pimps, police, rednecks, gaming men, pushers and the like, would have meant nothing *aesthetically,* for no amount of suffering will endow one with talent, just as no amount of practice will make up for the lack of a story.

Sentimentality has been something which African-American artists, whether folk or professional, have been fighting since slavery. Wallace Stevens once said that sentimentality, far from being an expression of feeling, was actually a failure of feeling — a contrived emotional excess. Beginning with the hymns that were passed on, as Eileen Southern brilliantly points out in *The Music of Black Americans,* the slaves not only changed the notes of the songs, but changed the words and often substituted starkly beautiful statements for the flowery phrases of the originals. This, of course, is the tradition out of which jazz comes vis-a-vis popular music. That is, though people have often thought that "jazzing something up" was synonymous with messing something up, it would be much better to say that, at its best, to jazz something up is to straighten it up, make it more humanly valuable rather than less.

...the night is cold, I'm so alone....

CENTRAL TO THE art of both Bessie Smith and Louis Armstrong was that gift, and it was passed on most effectively to Billie Holiday. Interestingly, very few people think of popular song when they think of Bessie Smith, for her repertoire was almost exclusively blues. But when she did take on a popular tune or a mock spiritual, her taste, rhythmic sense and ability to undercut the oppressive emptiness of the material was exemplary. Armstrong simply taught all the singers how to do what they had to do, whether directly or by extension. Billie Holiday was the first great female extension of his message, an artist who was able to personalize his innovations and come up with something of her own.

Even though her phrasing and sense of drama were rooted in those two giants, there was always something unique about Billie. She had one of the oddest sounds of any professional singer ever. When she was in her late teens (she was born in 1915), she began developing a following and caught the ear of John Hammond, who fought to get record dates for

an appreciation of billie holiday
by Stanley Crouch

her even though his associates in the record business thought she had no commercial appeal (understandable, given the very unusual timbre of her voice and her relaxed phrasing that predicted, as did the playing of Lester Young, what was later to be called the "cool school"). The thin vibrato and the small sound existed in sharp contrast to the big black ladies who shouted the blues, but had a charm for the discerning listener all its own.

Billie Holiday was an especially subtle singer, and that sense of raw and restrained statement, however contradictory that may seem, was not only paralleled by Lester Young, but also influenced by Miles Davis, another artist who created through introspection a style that could flare into a kind of chilling emotionality. Popular art was as straight-jacketing in many ways then as it is now and she was to share great camaraderie with Young, for he, too, had to fight the constant comparisons with Coleman Hawkins, Chu Berry, Ben Webster and the other big-toned tenor shouters.

Holiday was also attracted to Young and the other elegant black men of the thirties because of the romantic elements, the lyric reinterpretations of material, that were so important to the generation in which she emerged. It is almost as if they were creating an alternate set of standards — social, musical and personal — to the plantation images that were imposed on black artists by the media. They refuted the bubble-eyed, trembling, stuttering, minstrel figure with dignity, satire and elevated postures that included the most immaculate dress, providing panoramas of sophistication giving their audiences images of glamour which not only answered those of the silver screen, but at times exceeded them.

In many ways, the thirties were fascinating years because the Depression hung over everything and the American way to address that depression was to contradict it with a galaxy of romance, fantasy, adventure, with musicals, comedy, dance and those things that would allow audiences to forget about the hard times. Billie Holiday emerged during an era in which black artists began to become national stars, through recordings, radio, and personal appearances. These black artists began to learn, as Holiday did when she received a fan letter from Britain, that they were international figures as well as national ones. But Billie's new fortunes did not immediately improve the social circumstances surrounding her life. White entrepreneurs and managers began to emerge at the same time in the jazz world, and black performers often found themselves being dictated to by those who were supposedly in their employ. And racial prejudice, to be sure, didn't subside with Holiday's new-found success. John Chilton, in his biography *Billie's Blues*, tells of Billie once threating with a broken bottle a drunken white sailor who called her a nigger. But, too, Chilton says that when asked how she was doing, Billie would respond, "Well, you know, I'm still a nigger."

That she could explode about being called a name she would use to describe her own life's problems is indicative of the kind of ambivalence that gives her work value. Not that it is confused, but that it is almost always full of subtle contradictions or posits a deep knowledge of the vagaries of human experience, where a man can be a salvation or a burden, love a liberation from loneliness or a curse. Or they can exist at the very same time, a tension which is basic to African-American music, and extends the African combining of opposing forces as symbolized in the poly-rhythmic structures of the music with opposing emotion and phrasing. That is: one can easily see that jazz is a music in which the lyric content can be extremely melancholy while the rhythmic accompaniment can be exuberant, buoyant — *swinging;* this might be called an emotional double consciousness and it usually results in transcendence rather than synthesis. It is inherent to Billie Holiday's music.

One would do well to think about the broad suggestions of her repertoire and how that long list of songs and recordings comes together as a body of work. Just as Bessie Smith's recordings constitute a collected epic, a sense of ultimate national and personal verities, the same can be said about the work of Billie Holiday. Albert Murray writes in *The Hero and the Blues,* "What is created, expressed, performed, played, imitated, reproduced, reenacted, recounted, reflected and related in each instance is an anecdote which is assumed to represent the essential nature of existence among a given folk in a given community, community of faith, tradition, or nation; hence they are national epics."

What else can one call those recordings of Holiday's? They lament, they celebrate, they philosophize, they cajole, seduce, satirize, protest, question, laugh, cry, shatter invulnerability, or pose with stoic grace, and since they address aesthetic problems through the medium of improvisation, they propose to give the moment something it never has — order, which is the greatest contribution of jazz: it shows over and over that the present, the most anarchic region of experience, can be given perceivable form. This is achieved, by the way, through an extraordinary confidence in the decision-making capabilities of the individual as he or she functions within a group. Don't assume that Billie Holiday wasn't aware of these things, for in the following two quotes she gives as clear a sense of her aesthetics and her sense of national epics as anything you will get from verbose poetics:

No two people on earth are alike, and it's got to be that way in music, or it isn't music. I can't stand to sing the same song the same way two nights in succession, let alone two years or ten years. If you can, then it ain't music. It's close order drill, or exercise, or yodeling, or something, but it ain't music.

I've been told that nobody sings the word ''hunger'' like I do, or the word ''love.'' Maybe I want to remember what those words are all about — all the towns from coast to coast where I got my lumps and my scars — every damn bit of it. All I've learned in all those places from all those people is wrapped up in those two words. You've got to have something to eat and a little love in your life before you can hold still for any damn body's sermon on how to behave. Everything I am and everything I want out of life goes smack back to that.

It seems to me that in Billie Holiday we witness an exquisite blending of the sugars and salts of human experience stylized through song, with a domestic majesty that is equal to any form of human dignity in our ambivalent universe, where we will all, eventually, be having breakfast *with* the moles, or serve as breakfast *for* the moles.

Carlos Sampayo was born in 1943 in Buenos Aires, Argentina. He emigrated to Spain in 1972, where he worked as an advertising copywriter. Aside from his primary collaboration with José Muñoz, he has also written *El Hombre de la Nacional* for artist Jorge Zaffino, *Evaristo* for Francisco Solano Lopez, and several stories for Oscar Zarate.

José Muñoz was born in 1942 in Argentina and began his career as a cartoonist there as an assistant to the popular adventure artist Francisco Solano Lopez. In 1972, Muñoz moved to London to draw comics for a large English publisher. His collaboration with Carlos Sampayo began in 1974 and has continued to this day. Muñoz currently lives in Italy.

Muñoz & Sampayo

have been a team since *Alack Sinner,* their first graphic novel together. Alack Sinner is a burned-out detective whose early adventures were in a standard hard-boiled thriller mode, but who later became a vehicle for more personal and experimental work by Muñoz and Sampayo. Some of their books are *Sophie* (1978), *Joe's Bar* (1981), *Tango Milonga* (1986), *Sudor Sudaca* (1986), and *Nicaragua* (1986). Much of their work has appeared in English in the magazine *Sinner* (Fantagraphics Books), the graphic novel *Joe's Bar* (Catalan Communications), and *RAW* magazine.